P9-DNO-049

THE LEGEND OF ZELDA™
Manga Series

VOLUME 1	OCARINA OF TIME PART 1	...............ON SALE NOW!
VOLUME 2	OCARINA OF TIME PART 2	...............ON SALE NOW!
VOLUME 3	MAJORA'S MASK	............................ON SALE NOW!
VOLUME 4	ORACLE OF SEASONS	......................ON SALE NOW!
VOLUME 5	ORACLE OF AGES	............................ON SALE NOW!
VOLUME 6	FOUR SWORDS PART 1	....................ON SALE NOW!
VOLUME 7	FOUR SWORDS PART 2	....................ON SALE NOW!
VOLUME 8	THE MINISH CAP	............................ON SALE NOW!
VOLUME 9	A LINK TO THE PAST	......................ON SALE NOW!

Don't miss any of Link's exciting adventures!

PHANTOM HOURGLASS —THE GAME

The Legend of Zelda™: *Phantom Hourglass* was released in 2007 for the Nintendo DS. Utilizing the Nintendo DS platform, the game takes advantage of the stylus interface and 3-D cel-shaded graphics to bring players into the game world. Winner of several awards, *The Legend of Zelda*™: *Phantom Hourglass* has sold over four million copies worldwide.

THE LEGEND OF ZELDA
THE PHANTOM HOURGLASS

THE LEGEND OF ZELDA™
OF
PHANTOM HOURGLASS

CONTENTS

A LINK TO THE PAST

Chapter 1 Link and Tetra 5

Chapter 2 The Ghost Ship 13

Chapter 3 Linebeck the Sailor 29

Chapter 4 Isle of Ember 45

Chapter 5 Cannon Island 61

Chapter 6 Isle of Gust 77

Chapter 7 Molida Island 93

Chapter 8 Linebeck's Past and the Ghost Ship 109

Chapter 9 Tetra's True Identity 125

Chapter 10 Jolene the Pirate Girl 141

Chapter 11 A Confrontation with Bellum! 157

Chapter 12 The Final Battle! 173

SHSSH!!

SPLOOSH

CHAPTER 1
LINK AND
TETRA

YEAH!

DOLPHINS!

5

WHERE'RE YOU GOING, LINK?

YOU'RE NOT DONE SWABBING THE DECK!

BUT...

...THERE'RE DOLPHINS, TETRA!

WHY'D YOU SIGN ON TO THIS CREW ANYWAY?

THAT'S EASY!

THERE'RE *PLENTY* OF DOLPHINS IN THE OCEAN!

BIG DEAL!

7

...I CAN SHOW YOU MY SKILL WITH A SWORD... *AGAIN!*

OH, YOU WANNA FIGHT?!

OF COURSE, IF YOU'D RATHER FIGHT ME...

SURE, SHE *SAYS* SHE'S A PRINCESS... SHE'S SO BOSSY!

GRUMBLE

LET THEM GET THEIR EXERCISE.

THEY'RE AT IT AGAIN!

WHERE THE GHOST SHIP SAILS.

"THAT" AREA? WHAT AREA?

CAP'N!

LOTS OF SHIPS DISAPPEAR AROUND HERE.

GHOST SHIP?!

WE'LL BE ENTERING *THAT* AREA SOON!

8

11

TETRA, WAIT!

LET ME CHECK IT OUT!

WAIT HERE. I'LL PROVE IT'S NOT A GHOST SHIP.

SHOW SOME SPINE, NIKO!

TETRA!

NO! IT'S TOO DANGEROUS!

THAT'S AN ORDER.

YOU WAIT HERE, LINK.

EEEEK

HMPH!

SHOW YOURSELVES!

THEY MUST BE HIDING AROUND HERE.

...WENT INTO THE MAGICAL CASTLE WHERE THE MONSTER LIVED.

SO, TO RESCUE THE PRINCESS FROM HER CRYSTAL PRISON, THE HERO...

DON'T LEAVE US HANGING!

TELL US MORE!

HUH?!

...WILL CONTINUE TOMORROW.

AND WE...

THE BEACH!

CIELA, WHERE ARE YOU OFF TO?

THAT'S HOW THESE STORIES GO... THERE'S ALWAYS A CLIFF-HANGER!

HO HO

HEY! WHAT'S THAT?

AND TETRA?!

JOLT!

WAIT! WHERE'S THE GHOST SHIP?

SHSSHH

SHE CALLED FOR MY HELP!

...SAILED OFF WITH TETRA!

OH NO! THE GHOST SHIP...

MY GRANDPA... OSHUS!

...BUT GRANDPA MIGHT.

I DON'T KNOW MUCH ...

GRANDPA?

...NEVER COMES BACK.

TELL ME MORE!

BUT ANYONE ON THAT SHIP...

I'LL SHOW YOU THE WAY!

YES. YOU DO THAT, CIELA.

HE MAY KNOW MORE ABOUT THE GHOST SHIP. HE'S SAILED EVERY SEA THERE IS.

HE'S BEEN HERE BEFORE!

I KNOW HIS FACE!

C'MON! THIS WAY!

...

HE'S FINALLY HERE!

IT'S PRETTY RUNDOWN.

Whoa!

THIS IS THE TEMPLE OF THE OCEAN KING?

YEEK!

26

28

GRANDPA?! WHY ARE *YOU* HERE?

OLD MAN OSHUS ?!

THAT IS INDEED THE TREASURE.

IT'S THE PHANTOM HOUR-GLASS!

YOU'RE AWFULLY BRAVE, FOR ONE SO YOUNG.

YOU WENT INTO THE TEMPLE AND CAME OUT WITH THE TREASURE.

...YOUR LIFE CAN'T BE DRAINED UNTIL THE SAND RUNS OUT!

BUT IF YOU HAVE THIS HOUR-GLASS ...

IT SUCKS THE LIFE FROM THOSE WHO ENTER.

THIS TEMPLE IS UNDER A TERRIBLE CURSE.

40

TA-DAH

DON'T WORRY. WHEN IT COMES TO THE SEA, JUST LEAVE IT TO ME!

LET US SET SAIL IN SEARCH OF THE SAND OF HOURS!

YOU WANT TO FIND THE GHOST SHIP TO SAVE YOUR FRIEND!

SNIFF... THAT'S SO MOVING...

...I THINK I'LL CRY!

SOB

THEN HOW ARE YOU GOING TO GET ANYWHERE, BOY?

HMM...

YOU JUST WANT THE TREASURE!

NO ONE SAID *YOU* COULD COME ALONG!

WHEN DID YOU GET SO HELPFUL?

HOLD ON A MINUTE!

WAGGLE

BUT I'LL TAKE YOU ON AS CREW SO YOU SAIL FOR *FREE!*

...AND YOU'RE JUST A KID!

THAT TAKES MONEY, A LOT OF IT...

OR ARE YOU GOING TO CHARTER ONE?

UGH

DO YOU HAVE YOUR OWN SHIP?

SMIRK

CHAPTER 4 ISLE OF EMBER

CHUGCHUG CHUG

...ON THE SEAS OF ADVENTURE! HANG ON, TETRA! I'LL SAVE YOU SOON!

AT LAST WE'RE OFF...

SO GET MOVING!

DON'T FORGET YOU'RE ON THE CREW OF THE *S.S. LINEBECK* NOW!

YOU'VE GOT TO SWAB THE DECK!

WHAT'RE YOU LAZING AROUND FOR, BOY!

...

NOW DO THE LAUNDRY.

OKAY.

LINEBECK, THE DECK IS SWABBED!

THIS IS HOW ALL THIS GOT STARTED!

SCRUB

SCRUB

WASH YOUR **OWN** UNDERWEAR!

BOOT

REEEK

IT'S REALLY BEEN PILING UP.

WHY'VE I GOTTA TAKE ORDERS FROM THAT OLD GUY?!

THAT'S IT! I QUIT! THIS IS STUPID!

...YOU'LL NEVER BE A HERO WHO CAN SAVE HIS FRIEND.

...IF A CHALLENGE LIKE THIS IS TOO MUCH FOR YOU...

BESIDES...

UGH

IF YOU DON'T LIKE IT, THAT'S FINE. THEN PAY YOUR FARE.

IF YOU CAN'T, THEN GET OFF THE BOAT.

THANK YOU FOR FREEING ME FROM THE DARKNESS.

I AM LEAF, A SPIRIT OF POWER IN THE SERVICE OF THE GREAT SPIRIT THE OCEAN KING.

IT SEALED US AWAY. I WONDER WHAT HAPPENED TO THE OCEAN KING?

...BY A DEEP DARK-NESS.

A FEW YEARS AGO, THE OCEAN KING AND I WERE SET UPON...

THE SPIRIT YOU FREED BEARS PART OF THE POWER YOU NEED TO FIND THE GHOST SHIP.

SPLEN-DID! YOU DEFEATED THE POWER OF DARKNESS, LINK.

I DIDN'T TELL YOU ABOUT THE GHOST SHIP! HOW DID YOU KNOW?

A FORTUNE-TELLER SEES ALL.

Ho ho ho!

A RED FAIRY!

...LEARNED A LOT FROM YOUR CAPTAIN'S GOOD EXAMPLE!

GOOD JOB, BOY! CLEARLY YOU'VE...

THE REMAINING TWO GROW WEAKER. YOU MUST HURRY.

...YOU WILL KNOW WHERE TO FIND THE GHOST SHIP.

POWER, WISDOM, COURAGE... WHEN YOU HAVE ALL THREE SPIRITS...

ALL RIGHT! NOW, LEAF IS ON THE TEAM, TOO!

I WILL GLADLY ASSIST YOU, IF YOU LIKE.

I WISH HE ACTUALLY WOULD!

I SUPPOSE EVEN *HE* CAN BE OF HELP...

YOU BIG GREED HEAD!

YO-HO!

NOW WE'RE ONE STEP CLOSER TO THE TREASURE!

I DOUBT THAT.

YO-HOOOO!

IT MUST BE SHINY TREASURE WAITING FOR ME TO DISCOVER IT!

LIGHT TRAPPED IN THE DARK?

WHATEVER. LET'S HURRY TO THE NEXT ISLAND!

...BUT THEY'RE EXPENSIVE.

CAN YOU AFFORD IT?

OH, I'LL SELL YOU ONE...

SO YOU WANT TO BUY A CANNON?

PLEASE, SELL US ONE!

WE REALLY NEED IT!

NO, THAT'S NOT ENOUGH.

HEY, YOU CAN'T DO THAT ON YOUR OWN!

...10% OF ALL THE TREASURE WE FIND?

OH! WHAT IF WE GIVE YOU...

UMM...

FIFTY RUPEES!

YES!!

YOU WANNA HEAR?

HOW MUCH DO YOU WANT?

ARE YOU SURE?

69

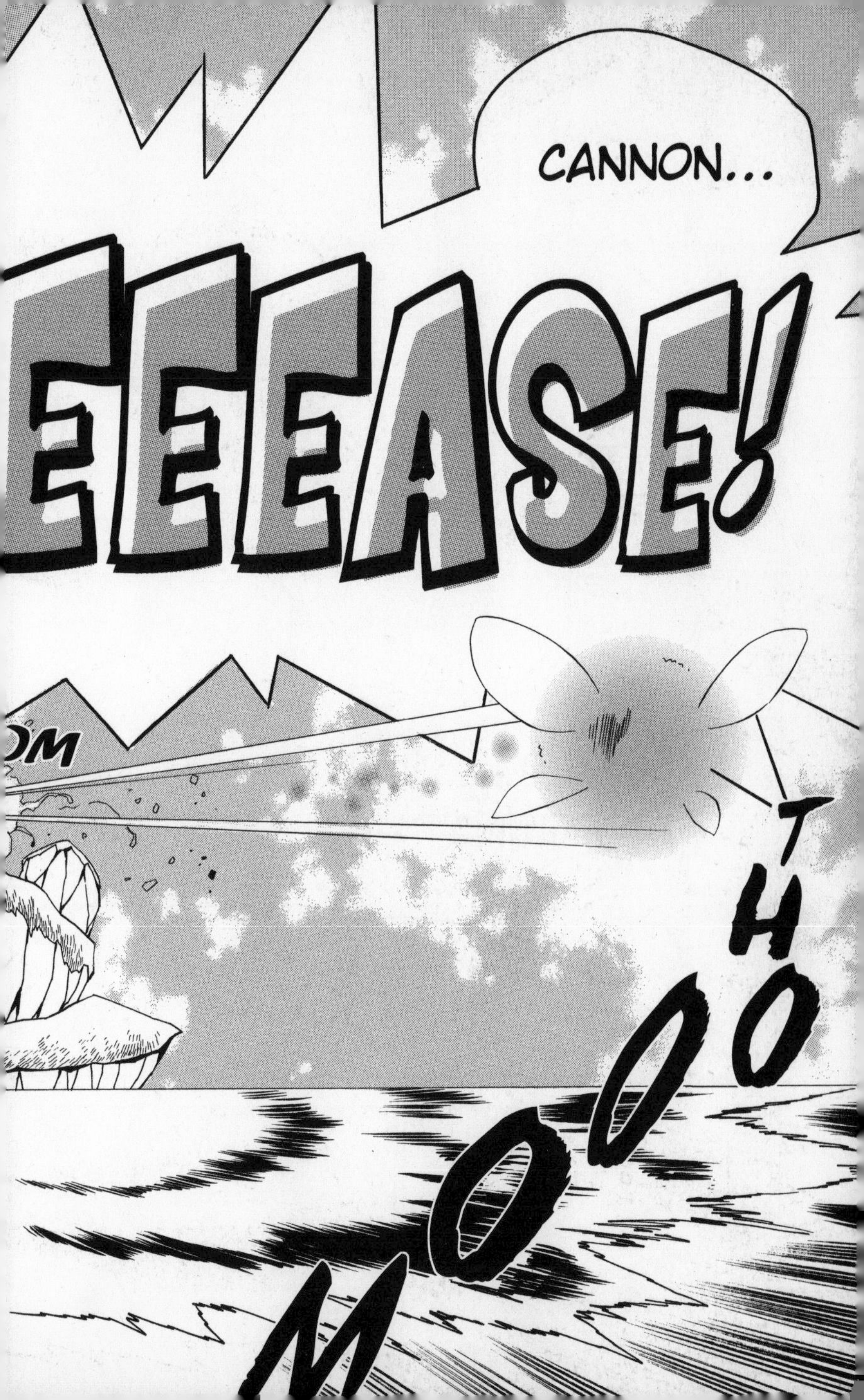
CANNON...
EEEASE!
OM
THOOOM

74

CIELA, WHERE ARE YOU?

UH...

... WHUH?

I'M RIGHT HERE!

YOU WON'T GET AWAY THIS TIME!

I CAN'T SEE ANY- THING!

NOTHING BUT PURE WHITE!

I'VE NEVER SEEN SUCH THICK FOG!

WHERE'S THE GHOST SHIP?

...THAT LEADS SHIPS ASTRAY WITH A MYS- TERIOUS POWER!

I'VE HEARD OF THIS BEFORE.

THE GHOST SHIP IS SUR- ROUNDED BY A THICK FOG...

IT'S LIKE IT'S MOCKING US! IT APPEARED...

...THEN DISAP- PEARED!

ARGH! NO!

NO! STOP!

HERE, DRINK THIS.

WATER?

WATER...

Mumph...

WE'RE ALMOST OUT!

Don't ignore me!

DO YOU LIVE HERE?

ARE YOU ALONE?

...

WHAT'S YOUR NAME?

DID THE FOG BRING YOU HERE, TOO?

...

...OR LORELEI...

...THERE TO LURE YOU TO YOUR DOOM!

WHEN YOU'RE ADRIFT AND COME ACROSS A LONE GIRL, THERE'S A 90% CHANCE THAT SHE'S...

...A VAMPIRE...

WHISPERING

WHAT IS?

REALLY? THAT'S BAD.

IT'S LIKE SHE'S AN EMPTY SHELL.

SOMETHING'S WRONG WITH HER.

GLUB

GLUB

BLUB

THEY DEFEATED THE CYCLOK.

ARROGANT FEEDER FISH! I'LL NOT FORGIVE THIS.

SHEEN

...THE DEEP SEA... *AWAKEN!*

CRAYK! DEEP ASLEEP IN...

GWOOM

YOUR CLAWS CAN SHATTER ROCKS. USE THEM...

...TO CRUSH THESE INTER-LOPERS!

LINK! THE MONSTER LEFT A SEA CHART.

WHERE IS MOLIDA ISLAND?

ZWOOOOSH

...AND HERE'S MOLIDA ISLAND!

THE ISLE OF GUST IS HERE...

WAIT!

FWIP

SHIK

ABSOLUTELY NOT.

SORRY. NO CAN DO.

TO THE SOUTHWEST-ERN SEA! LINEBECK, PREPARE THE SHIP FOR—

WHY WOULD I FIGHT A MONSTER JUST TO SAVE ONE LITTLE GIRL?

IF YOU WANT TO GO, GO ALONE.

SHE HAS NO CONNECTION TO THE TREASURE OR THE GHOST SHIP.

YOU WON'T HELP HER?!

?!

THAT GIRL IS IN TROUBLE!

THAT'S THE ISLAND!

A MONSTER CAME ASHORE! I THINK I PEED MY PANTS!

A MONSTER!

ISLANDERS RUNNING THIS WAY.

Gyah! Eeek!

?!

HELP US!

HURRY!

IF THE MONSTE HOLDS ANY SA OF HOURS, WE HAVE TO FIGHT ANYWAY!

LOOK! IT'S THE GIRL!

AH!

IS IT MAKING A... NEST?!

CIELA ...

I'M SORRY I HID THE TRUTH FOR SO LONG.

HUH?

YOU ARE THE THIRD FAIRY ...

...THE SPIRIT OF COURAGE.

...A SPIRIT?!

CIELA IS...

SHE IS YOUR LOST MEMORY.

AND THAT GIRL ...

SHE MAY LOOK HUMAN, BUT THAT'S JUST A DISGUISE.

RETURN TO YOUR ORIGINAL FORM.

LINK DEFEATED CRAYK. NOW NO ONE CAN THREATEN YOU.

WHEN THE OCEAN KING WAS SEALED IN DARKNESS, HE HELPED YOU ESCAPE BY SEVERING YOUR SPIRIT MEMORY.

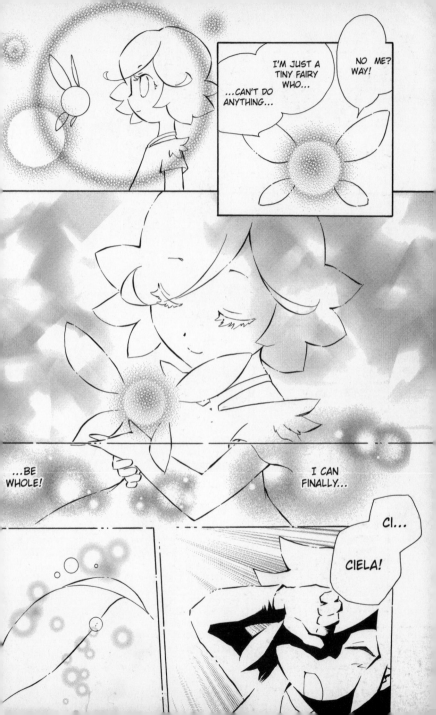

NOW YOU MUST SAVE TETRA, AND QUICKLY!

MY STORY CAN WAIT.

GET ON, BOY!

HOW ARE YOU RELATED TO THE OCEAN KING?

WHAT ABOUT YOU, OLD MAN OSHUS?

HARD APORT!!

...GHOST SHIP!

YOU WON'T ESCAPE ME THIS TIME...

CHAPTER 8 — LINEBECK'S PAST AND THE GHOST SHIP

FSSHH

LINEBEEECK
...

LINE-
BECK,
COME
BACK!

GAAAY

HAAAA

LINEBECK!

LINEBECK?

THE GHOST
SHIP IS
ANCHORED TO
STARBOARD!

LINEBECK,
ARE YOU
LISTENING?!

DROP THE
ANCHOR!
HURRY!

ALL RIGHT, LET'S GO!

TETRA'S THERE! I CAN FEEL IT!

SHIVER QUAKE TREMBLE

YOU GO ON.

BOY...

I'LL WAIT...

...HERE ON THE SHIP.

...WHILE YOU WAIT HERE, LINEBECK, YOU SCAREDY... ERRR... YOU COLDY-CAT!

THEN WE GET THE TREASURE FOR OURSELVES...

BUT YOU WANT THE GHOST SHIP'S TREASURE, DON'T YOU?

AGAIN ?!

AND I NEED TO PEE.

I'M JUST...A LITTLE COLD.

113

WELL, WE'RE GOING.

FWIP FWIP

...AND BARK AT ME!

QUIET, PIP-SQUEAK!

USUALLY HE'D SAY...

...BE CAREFUL.

OKAY...

YOU GOT A FEVER?

LINEBECK'S *CONCERNED* ABOUT US?!

Did he say "be careful"?

L-LINE-BECK...

KONK

GET GOING!

SHUT UP!

FWIIIP

NO, WAIT.

ON SECOND THOUGHT, I'LL GO TOO.

CHUNK

BOY...

ANY-
THING
COULD
JUMP
OUT AT
US...

HE'S
ACTING SO
STRANGE!

WHAT'S
GOING
ON WITH
LINEBECK?

THERE
ARE
THREE
LEVELS
INSIDE.

IF
THERE'S
A TOUGH
MONSTER...

THAT'S
THE
ENTRANCE
TO THE
CABIN.

...USE THE
WEAPON
HIDDEN IN THE
BARREL ON
THE BOTTOM
DECK.

TETRA!

I WAS KIDNAPPED BY THE GHOST SHIP...

I AM ONE OF THE CUBUS SISTERS.

ARE YOU TETRA'S FRIENDS?

...BUT THOUGH I WAS ALSO KIDNAPPED, TETRA RESCUED ME.

IS SHE ALIVE?

SH-SHE'S BEEN TURNED TO STONE!

THE LIVING DEAD BELOW DECK.

WHO DID THIS TO TETRA?

SOB SOB SOB

SHE WAS CURSED!

WAAAAH

TETRA TOOK MY PLACE AND WAS TURNED TO STONE!

YOU'RE AS TRICKY AS EVER.

...THE COWARD, LINEBECK?

OH MY! IS THAT...

HOW MAY SAILORS HAVE YOU LURED IN LIKE THAT?

?!

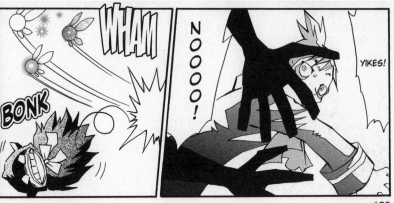

122

123

124

FSHOOM

SHINK

RETURN TO DARKNESS, AND DON'T COME BACK!

TETRA!

TETRA!

SHE TURNED BACK TO STONE!

SPSSS

GET AWAY FROM HER!

A G-GHOST!

SHE'S POSSESSED BY THE DEAD!

BACK OFF!

TETRA IS REALLY PRINCESS ZELDA IN DISGUISE!

LINEBECK, THAT WASN'T A GHOST.

130

HUH?!

HO HO

I HAD A HUNCH HE MIGHT BE.

GRANDPA'S THE OCEAN KING?!

YOU FIGURED IT OUT?

WHAT A SMART LAD.

THIS IS JUST... ...A DISGUISE. I AM THE OCEAN KING, THE GREAT SPIRIT WHO RULES THIS OCEAN.

LINK, YOU DID WELL COMING THIS FAR.

I SEE YOU HAVE THE SPIRIT OF A TRUE HERO.

...A MONSTER APPEARED OUT OF NOWHERE AND ATTACKED.

THEN SEVERAL YEARS AGO...

WHAT HAPPENED TO YOUR OCEAN?

NOW...

I CAN TELL YOU EVERYTHING.

THIS OCEAN WAS ORIGINALLY RICH AND OVERFLOWING WITH FORCE ENERGY.

...BUT WHEN I ATTACKED...

I FOUGHT HIM...

...A HORRIBLE MONSTER THAT ATE FORCE ENERGY.

HIS NAME WAS BELLUM...

...HE DRAINED EVEN MY ENERGY. HE BEAT ME AND SEALED ME DEEP BELOW A TEMPLE.

...BELLUM WANTS EVERY BIT OF FORCE HE CAN FIND IN OTHER CREATURES, INCLUDING HUMANS.

NOT SATISFIED WITH JUST THE FORCE HE DRAINED FROM ME...

EVEN NOW HE'S DRAINING FORCE FROM ME.

I CAN BARELY HOLD THIS FORM TOGETHER.

...THEN IT DEVOURS ALL THEIR FORCE!

THIS GHOST SHIP IS A MONSTER CREATED BY BELLUM. RUMORS OF TREASURE DRAW HUMANS TO IT...

LADY TETRA'S SPIRIT IS FILLED WITH FORCE ENERGY, SO OF COURSE HE WANTS IT.

HE PROBABLY TURNED HER TO STONE BECAUSE HE COULDN'T DRAIN HER COMPLETELY.

Umph!

SO TO RETURN TETRA TO NORMAL...

...I NEED TO BEAT BELLUM?

THAT'S RIGHT! IF YOU DEFEAT HIM...

...AND BRING THE SAND OF HOURS TO ME...

...I CAN RESTORE LADY TETRA'S FORCE ENERGY!

THE SAND OF HOURS CRYSTALLIZED FORCE AND THE SOURCE..

...OF MY POWER. BELLUM USED IT TO GIVE LIFE TO HIS MONSTERS.

VISIT THE BLACKSMITH, ZAUZ, WHO LIVES IN THE NORTHWESTERN SEA.

HE WILL TEACH YOU HOW TO DEFEAT BELLUM.

GOT IT!

ZAUZ, GOT IT!

WE'LL SET SAIL RIGHT AWAY!

YOU REGRET WHAT YOU DID...

...AND WANT TO SET THINGS RIGHT. RIGHT?

...SO YOU CAN MAKE UP FOR BETRAYING YOUR SHIPMATES, RIGHT?

I BET YOU'VE BEEN LOOKING FOR THE GHOST SHIP ALL THIS TIME...

HMPH.

YOU'RE WRONG.

TRUST ME AND I'LL BETRAY YOU.

GOT THAT, BRAT?!

I'M JUST GREEDY, SELFISH, COWARDLY LINEBECK!

...IS THE TREASURE THE GHOST SHIP IS CARRYING!

WHAT I WANT...

THAT'S THE KIND OF MAN I AM!

TETRA ALWAYS SAID THAT THE CREW OF A SHIP HAS TO WORK TOGETHER!

WHATEVER KIND OF MAN YOU WERE...

...WE ONLY GOT THIS FAR BECAUSE OF THE CAPTAIN OF THE S.S. LINEBECK!

I'LL LEND YOU MY STRENGTH TO GET YOUR TREASURE...

SMAP

...THEN YOU CAN LEND YOUR STRENGTH TO OUR FIGHT!

BUT IF YOU HELP LINK TO DEFEAT HIM...

...BUT AS LONG AS BELLUM CONTROLS THE SHIP, WE CAN'T GET IT.

I WANT THE TREA- SURE...

DON'T LOOK AT ME WITH THOSE BIG EYES! HOW CORNY CAN YOU GET?! SHEESH!

...I WILL GRANT YOU ONE WISH.

HOW DOES THAT SOUND?

UMPH GAH

137

SURE IT'S KINDA UGLY, BUT...

WELL HE *HAS* A FACE.

?

FACE IS IMPORTANT FOR A SEA CAPTAIN. LET HIM PUT ON A SHOW.

STOP NATTERING AND GET ON BOARD!

HARD TO STARBOARD!

TO THE NORTH-WESTERN SEA!

FWIK

138

LOOKS NICE!

I BET YOU MISSED THAT, EH, TETRA?

THERE.

WE'LL GO DEFEAT BELLUM AND GET YOU BACK TO NOR—

IT WON'T BE LONG NOW.

WE'LL STAY WITH YOU THE REST OF THE WAY.

WHAT ARE YOU DOING, BOY?

WE'RE UNDER ATTACK!

WHAT WAS THAT?!

WH...

ACK!

WHUMP

BOOM

IT'S NO USE HIDING HIM. I KNOW...

HMPH.

I DON'T KNOW.

...AND TELL ME WHERE LINEBECK IS, OKAY? BE A GOOD LITTLE BOY...

D'OH!

YOU WON'T GET AWAY THIS TIME, COWARD.

...WHAT KIND OF MAN HE IS!

...RUBS MY HEART THE WRONG WAY!

THAT QUESTION...

WHAT DID I DO TO DESERVE THIS?

WAIT! WAIT!

CALM DOWN, JOLENE.

TAKE IT! HERE! ...

That's three years old!

SQUID JERKY

YIPE!

DON'T TREAT ME LIKE A FOOL!

WHAT KIND OF A WOMAN GETS SO MAD ABOUT SOME STOLEN SQUID JERKY?

I DIDN'T TAKE ANYTHING ELSE.

WHADDA YA WANT THEN?

HOW SHE FEELS?

YOU NEED TO BE MORE SENSITIVE TO HOW SHE FEELS.

LINEBECK, YOU REALLY ARE AN IDIOT.

...

THAT'S NOT WHAT I'M *REALLY* MAD ABOUT!

JERK!

149

HUH?!

...BECAUSE YOU LEFT WITHOUT SAYING ANYTHING!

SHE'S NOT MAD ABOUT THE SQUID! SHE'S MAD...

RIDICULOUS! WHO'D CARE ABOUT THAT LOSER?

IT DIDN'T FEEL RIGHT BEING MISTAKEN FOR A HERO.

I'M A COWARD WHO TURNS ON HIS FRIENDS.

WHY?

...WHEN SHE LIKES YOU SO MUCH.

LINEBECK, WHY DID YOU SNEAK OFF...

TOO DIRECT

WHO SAID I LIKE HIM?!

...ON HIS LAST SHIP.

HE REGRETS ABANDONING HIS COMRADES...

150

LINEBECK!

!

THIS ONE...

...IS *EASY* TO POS-SESS...

...EASY TO MOVE.

KLANK

KLANK

...YOUR FORCE!

I WILL USE HIM TO STEAL..

LET LINEBECK GO!

FSHH

WAIT!

HE'S GONE!

...THE HOURGLASS TO THE TEMPLE.

IF YOU WOULD SAVE THIS MAN, BRING...

WHAT'S GOING TO HAPPEN TO LINEBECK?!

WHAT'S GOING ON?

THE TEMPLE OF THE OCEAN KING?!

TEMPLE

JOLENE, I NEED TO ASK A FAVOR.

YOU CAN COUNT ON ME! THEN I'LL MEET YOU...

...AT MERCAY ISLAND!

CAN YOU FIND ZAUZ THE BLACKSMITH AND ASK HOW TO DEFEAT BELLUM?

WE'RE GOING BACK TO MERCAY ISLAND!

THIS TIME IT COULD FINISH YOU.

YOUR WEAK WILL HAS COST YOU SO MUCH OVER THE YEARS.

LINEBECK, YOU LOSER...

FAITH IN US...AND IN LINEBECK!

DON'T THINK THAT!

HAVE FAITH, JOLENE!

I NEED THAT SWORD AS SOON AS POSSIBLE!

...GO HAVE SOME TEA.

IT'S A DIFFICULT PROCESS. WHY DON' YOU...

HURRY!

UNGH GROAN

UNGH GRUNT

STUPID EYE MONSTER, YOU CAN'T JUST USE PEOPLE'S BODIES!

SHUT UP!

LINE-BECK...?

WHAT ARE YOU DOING?!

HOL ON

I NEVER HAD A FIRST MATE...

...BUT WE MADE A GOOD TEAM.

IT WAS G-GREAT SAILING WITH YOU.

LINK!

...I'D NEVER FORGIVE MYSELF.

...MADE ME HURT YOU...

IF BELLUM...

WHEN YOU GROW UP, DON'T BECOME...

...A WORTHLESS MAN LIKE ME!

I C-CAN'T TEACH YOU MUCH...

...BUT LISTEN.

NOW ISN'T THE TIME TO START USING MY REAL NAME!

NO!

AS THE SPIRIT OF COURAGE YOU CAN MAKE ONE!

A PHANTOM SPHERE!

EVERYTHING HAS STOPPED!

THAT'S WEIRD.

?

HM?

THE MEMORIES THAT BELLUM SEALED AWAY ARE COMING BACK!

IF YOU PLACE A PHANTOM SPHERE INTO THE HOURGLASS, YOU CAN STOP TIME!

THAT'S RIGHT!

I REMEMBER, LINK! THAT'S MY TRUE POWER!

KERSPLASH

...AND TO RESCUE YOU.

AS BELLUM'S POWER WEAKENED, SO DID MY PRISON. I WAS ABLE TO RETURN TO MY TRUE FORM...

GASP

IS *THAT* WHAT YOU REALLY LOOK LIKE?

O- OLD.. MAN?

GASP

ISN'T THIS GREAT, LINK?

YIPPEE!

THANKS FOR EVERY-THING YOU DID!

I THOUGHT ABOUT YOU THE WHOLE TIME I WAS STONE.

HUH?!

ZLRRSH

BLOOSH

GASP

WHAT HAPPENED, LINK?

W-WHERE ARE WE?

ZSSHH

ZSSHH

WAS THERE ANY TREASURE?

WHAT HAPPENED ON THE GHOST SHIP?

AHOY!

CAP'N!

WELL, SINCE I WAS...

186

BUT WHAT ABOUT *YOU* GUYS?! WHY DIDN'T YOU COME AFTER ME?!

LINK SAILED THE SEAS AND FOUGHT MONSTERS TO RESCUE ME!

...HELD PRISONER ON THE GHOST SHIP I DON'T REALLY KNOW!

...SINCE YOU WENT ABOARD THE GHOST SHIP!

IT'S ONLY BEEN ABOUT TEN MINUTES...

W-WHAT ARE YOU TALKING ABOUT, CAP'N?

...ALL A DREAM?

WAS IT...

DID YOU HIT YOUR HEAD?

T-TEN MINUTES?

MAYBE LINEBECK DIDN'T WISH FOR TREASURE AFTER ALL...

THAT STEAM WHISTLE ...!

DASH

YO-HOOOO!

■THE END■

POKÉMON®
DIAMOND AND PEARL ADVENTURE!

A BRAND NEW QUEST

Can a new trainer and his friends track down the legendary Pokémon Dialga before it's too late?

Story and Art by
Shigekatsu Ihara

Find out in the *Pokémon Diamond and Pearl Adventure* manga—buy yours today!

On sale at store.viz.com
Also available at your local bookstore or comic store.